D1616625

An Open Adoption Story

Learning About
My Friend's
Adoption

Written by Allison Olson

Illustrated by Darlee Urbiztondo

Illustrations by Darlee Urbiztondo
Book Layout and Design by Praise Saflor

Publisher's Cataloging-in-Publication data

Names: Olson, Allison, author. | Urbiztondo, Darlee, illustrator.
Title: Learning about my friend's adoption : an open adoption story /
written by Allison Olson; illustrated by Darlee Urbiztondo.
Series: An Open Adoption Story
Description: West Linn, OR: Kids are Awesome Publishing, LLC, 2023. | Summary: Curious young
boy finds out that his friend is adopted, his head is filled with questions. Listening to his friend's story
starts a journey towards a better understanding of adoption.
Identifiers: LCCN: 2023911016 | ISBN: 979-8-9851629-6-7 (hardcover) |
979-8-9851629-5-0 (paperback) | 979-8-9851629-7-4 (epub)
Subjects: LCSH Adoption--Juvenile fiction. | Friendship--Juvenile fiction. |
Family-Juvenile fiction. | BISAC JUVENILE FICTION / Family / Adoption
Classification: LCC PZ7.1 .O47 Le 2023 | DDC [E]--dc23

For Braxtyn

You light up our lives

Can I tell you about something I learned today
from my friend? She is just like you and me.

She likes to build rocket ships,
dance, and play dress up.

6

She has a family like me, except it's a
little different because she was adopted.
I asked her what it means to be adopted,
so she told me her story...

"Being adopted means I have one mom that carried me in her belly before I was born. She is my birth mom.

And I also have a mommy and daddy who tuck me into bed each night, wake me up in the morning, and cheer me on at soccer practice. They are my adoptive parents. I call them Mommy and Daddy."

9

"So you have two moms?"

"Yes, but more than that
I have two families."

"I have grandparents, aunts, uncles, and cousins in both families."
"I stay in touch with them through texts, pictures, and visits—just like you do with your family."

"Do you love both of your families?"

14

My friend giggled. "Yes, of course I love them both—just like you love your family."

15

"Through an adoption agency. My mommy and daddy filled out a lot of papers and waited, hoping to be chosen to be my parents."

17

"There were lots of people who wanted to raise me. Other families that had been waiting years for a child too.

18

It was really important to my birth mom
to pick the right family out of all of them."

"She looked through pictures and descriptions of all of the families until finally...

20

...she picked my parents!"

"My mommy and daddy tell me all the time how lucky THEY were to be chosen."

22

"Wow! I didn't realize that's how it worked."

"Yep, that's my adoption story.

24

The best thing of all is
that I love both families—
and they love me."

25

"Wow! That's cool! I know there
are lots of ways to build a family...

26

and now I know about open adoption.
Thank you for explaining it to me.
I'm happy to have a friend like you."

I never knew that some people have two families. It's pretty cool that we are all different in our own ways and that adoption is one of the ways that makes my friend special. I'm glad she is my friend.

29

Draw Your Family Here (don't forget any pets!)

Stay in touch!
Visit our website and join our email list at

www.ouradoptionbooks.com.
Share your family drawings and
tell us what you love doing together as a family.

Get the whole Surrounded by Love: An Open Adoption Story collection,
Activity Book, Keepsake Journal, Stickers, Bookmark, and Plushie.

Author Bio

Being both an adoptee and an adoptive parent, Allison Olson has a unique perspective on the topic of adoption. Her goal is to build confidence and self-esteem in young adoptees by changing the adoption narrative from the "lucky" child to the "loved" child. Allison lives in Oregon with her husband, two daughters, and their two kittens Bo and Aero. This book follows Allison's highly successful first book on adoption, *Surrounded by Love: An Open Adoption Story*.

Illustrator Bio

Darlee is a multi-disciplinary, creative artist based in the Philippines. She is known as Happylee. She is proficient in digital illustrations, painting, calligraphy, graphic design, and traditional art. She has put her imagination and her heart into this project, as she has a big brother who is adopted and loved so much. Darlee believes that her art is an extension of herself and her soul.

Printed in the USA
CPSIA information can be obtained
at www.ICGtesting.com
JSHW071037160923
48209JS00003B/19